U2//

HOW TO DISMANTLE AN ATOMIC BOMB

Exclusive Distributors:
Music Sales Limited
Distribution Centre, Newmarket Road, Bury St. Edmunds,
Suffolk IP33 3YB, England.
Music Sales Pty Limited
120 Rothschild Avenue, Rosebery, NSW 2018, Australia.

Order No. AM91769
ISBN 0-7119-3890-3
This book © Copyright 2004 by Universal Music Publishing.

Music arranged by Matt Cowe & Arthur Dick.
Music processed by Paul Ewers Music Design.
Cover design by Shaughn McGrath, Four5One Creative, Dublin.
Printed in the United Kingdom.

Your Guarantee of Quality
As publishers, we strive to produce every book to the highest
commercial standards. The music has been freshly engraved and,
whilst endeavouring to retain the original running order of the recorded
album, the book has been carefully designed to minimise awkward page
turns and to make playing from it a real pleasure.
Particular care has been given to specifying acid-free, neutral-sized paper
made from pulps which have not been elemental chlorine bleached.
This pulp is from farmed sustainable forests and was produced with
special regard for the environment. Throughout, the printing and binding
have been planned to ensure a sturdy, attractive publication which
should give years of enjoyment.If your copy fails to meet our high
standards, please inform us and we will gladly replace it.

www.musicsales.com

www.U2com

VERTIGO//9
MIRACLE DRUG//16
SOMETIMES YOU CAN'T MAKE IT
ON YOUR OWN//24
LOVE AND PEACE OR ELSE//42
CITY OF BLINDING LIGHTS//33
ALL BECAUSE OF YOU//48
A MAN AND A WOMAN//62
CRUMBS FROM YOUR TABLE//55
ONE STEP CLOSER//68
ORIGINAL OF THE SPECIES//74
YAHWEH//80
FAST CARS//88

GUITAR TABLATURE EXPLAINED

Guitar music can be notated three different ways: on a musical stave, in tablature, and in rhythm slashes

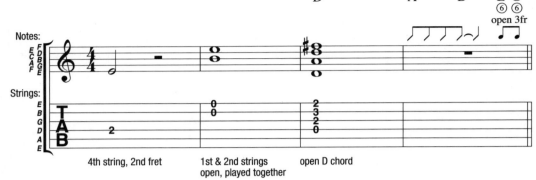

RHYTHM SLASHES are written above the stave. Strum chords in the rhythm indicated. Round noteheads indicate single notes.

THE MUSICAL STAVE shows pitches and rhythms and is divided by lines into bars. Pitches are named after the first seven letters of the alphabet.

TABLATURE graphically represents the guitar fingerboard. Each horizontal line represents a string, and each number represents a fret.

4th string, 2nd fret   1st & 2nd strings open, played together   open D chord

DEFINITIONS FOR SPECIAL GUITAR NOTATION

SEMI-TONE BEND: Strike the note and bend up a semi-tone (1/2 step).

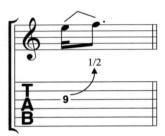

WHOLE-TONE BEND: Strike the note and bend up a whole-tone (whole step).

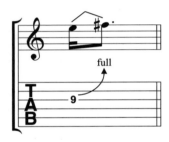

GRACE NOTE BEND: Strike the note and bend as indicated. Play the first note as quickly as possible.

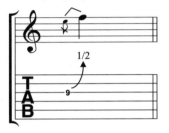

QUARTER-TONE BEND: Strike the note and bend up a 1/4 step.

BEND & RELEASE: Strike the note and bend up as indicated, then release back to the original note.

COMPOUND BEND & RELEASE: Strike the note and bend up and down in the rhythm indicated.

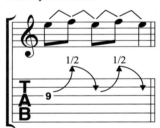

PRE-BEND: Bend the note as indicated, then strike it.

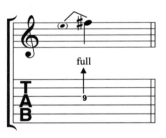

PRE-BEND & RELEASE: Bend the note as indicated. Strike it and release the note back to the original pitch.

HAMMER-ON: Strike the first note with one finger, then sound the second note (on the same string) with another finger by fretting it without picking.

PULL-OFF: Place both fingers on the notes to be sounded, strike the first note and without picking, pull the finger off to sound the second note.

LEGATO SLIDE (GLISS): Strike the first note and then slide the same fret-hand finger up or down to the second note. The second note is not struck.

MUFFLED STRINGS: A percussive sound is produced by laying the fret hand across the string(s) without depressing, and striking them with the pick hand.

NATURAL HARMONIC: Strike the note while the fret-hand lightly touches the string directly over the fret indicated.

PICK SCRAPE: The edge of the pick is rubbed down (or up) the string, producing a scratchy sound.

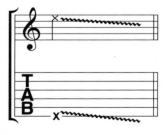

PALM MUTING: The note is partially muted by the pick hand lightly touching the string(s) just before the bridge.

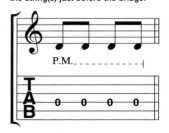

SHIFT SLIDE (GLISS & RESTRIKE): Same as legato slide, except the second note is struck.

NOTE: The speed of any bend is indicated by the music notation and tempo.

Vertigo

Words & Music by U2

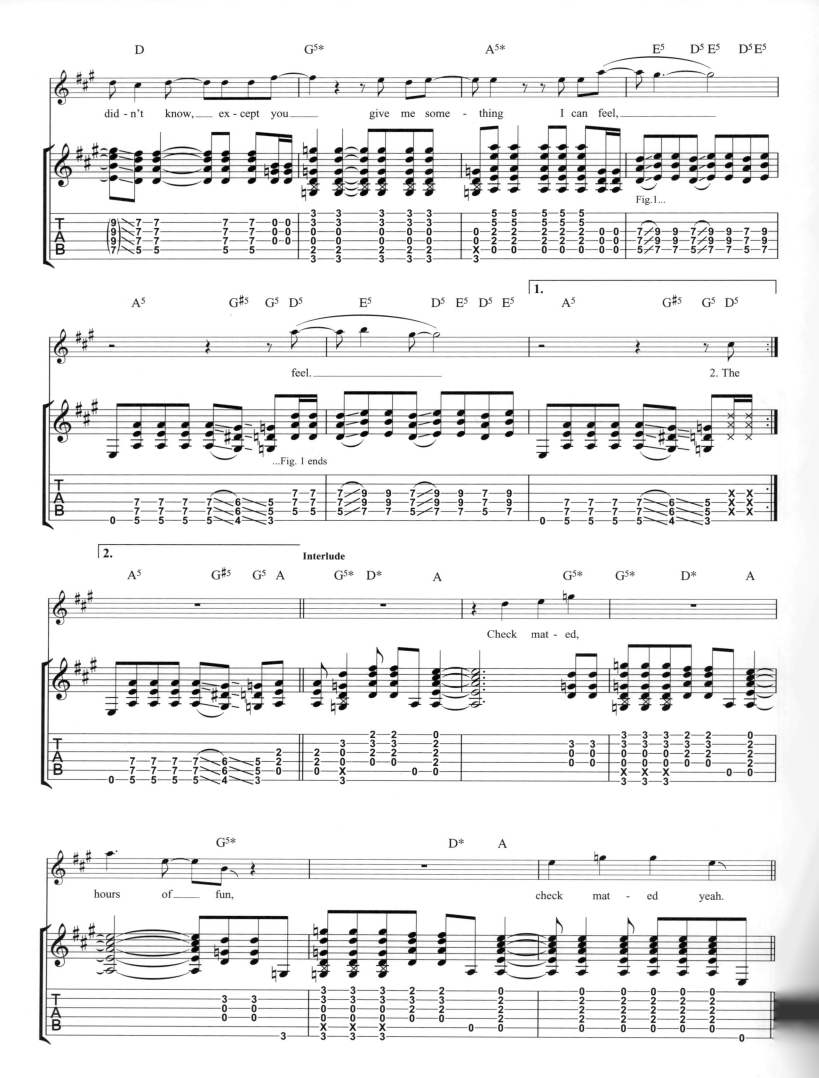

Miracle Drug

Words by Bono
Music by U2

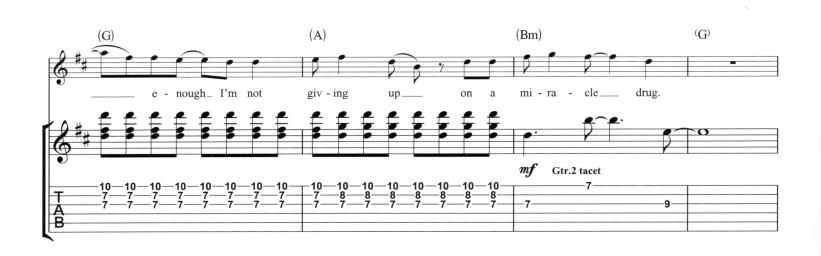

_____ e - nough__ I'm not giv - ing up____ on a mi - ra - cle___ drug.

mf **Gtr.2 tacet**

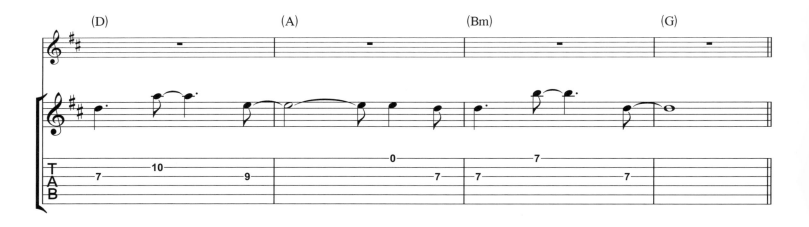

Verse

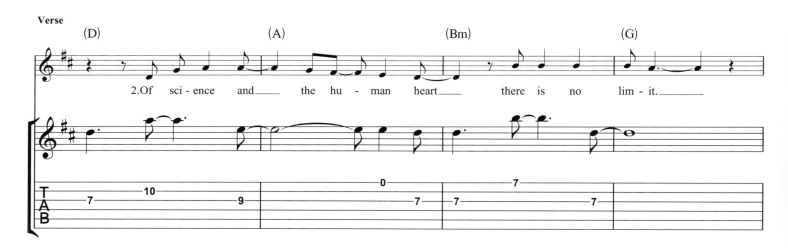

2.Of sci - ence and____ the hu - man heart____ there is no lim - it._____

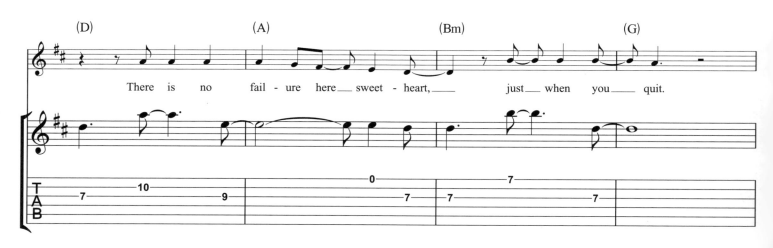

There is no fail - ure here__ sweet - heart,____ just__ when you__ quit.

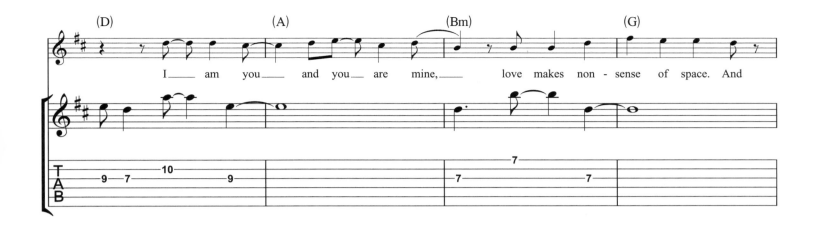

I___ am you___ and you___ are mine,___ love makes non- sense of space. And

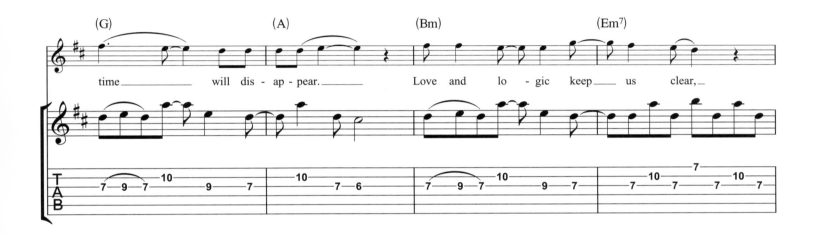

time_____ will dis - ap - pear.___ Love and lo - gic keep___ us clear,___

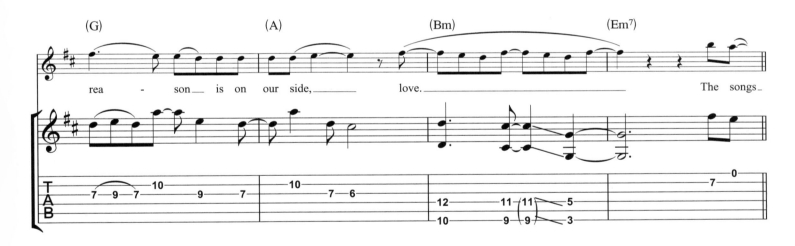

rea - son___ is on our side,___ love._____ The songs___

Chorus

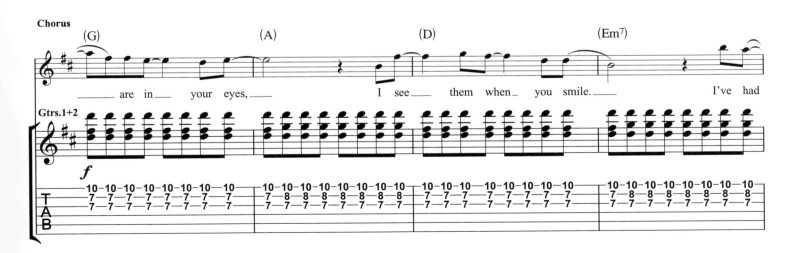

___ are in___ your eyes,___ I see___ them when___ you smile.___ I've had

19

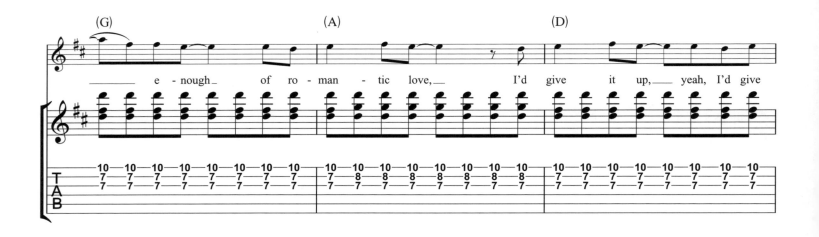

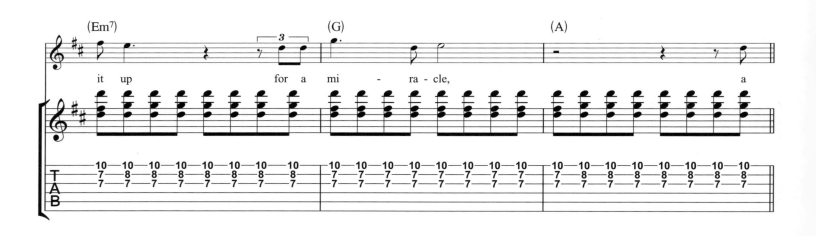

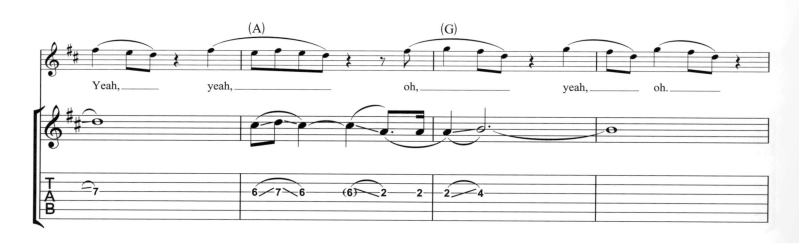

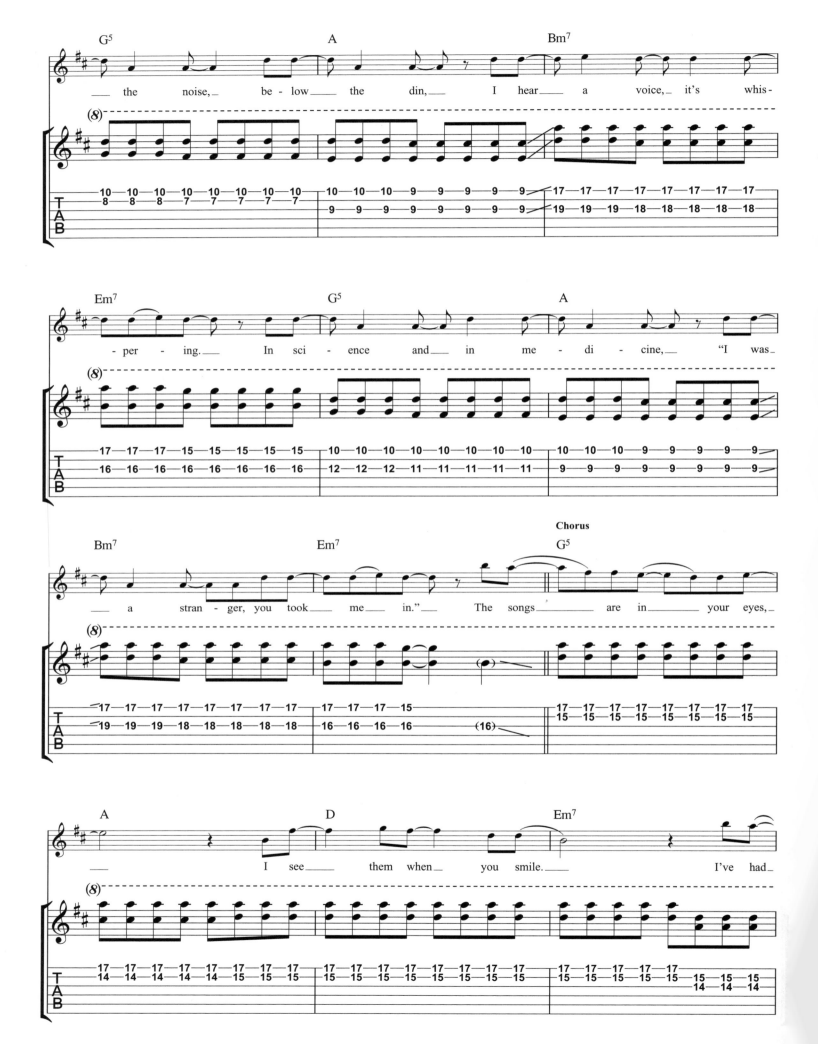

Sometimes You Can't Make It On Your Own

Words by Bono
Music by U2

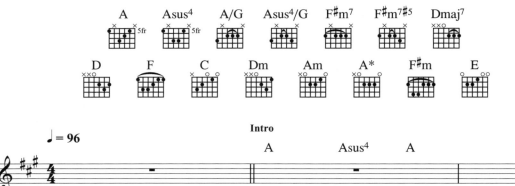

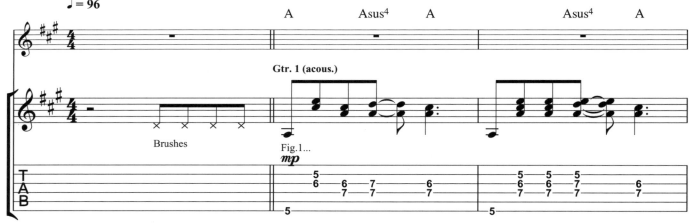

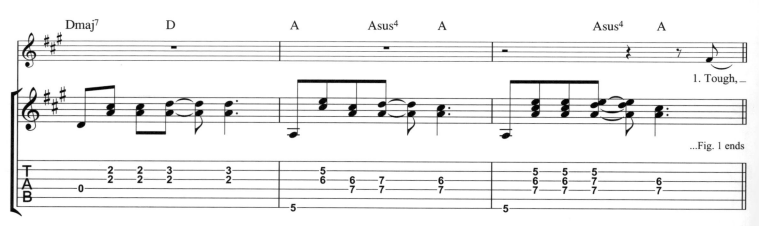

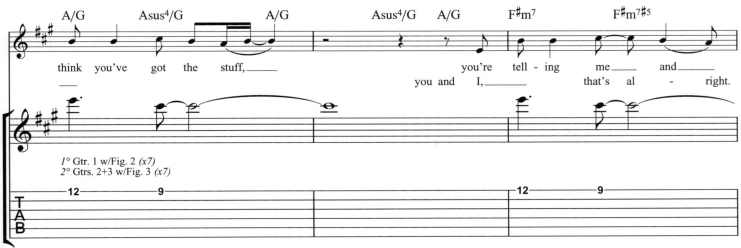

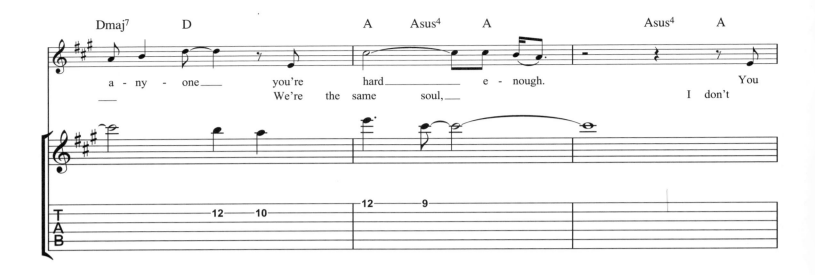

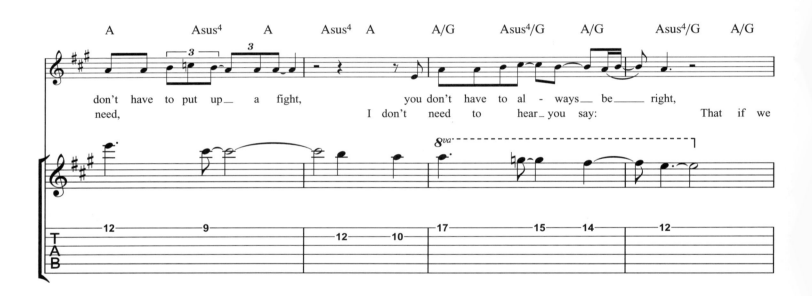

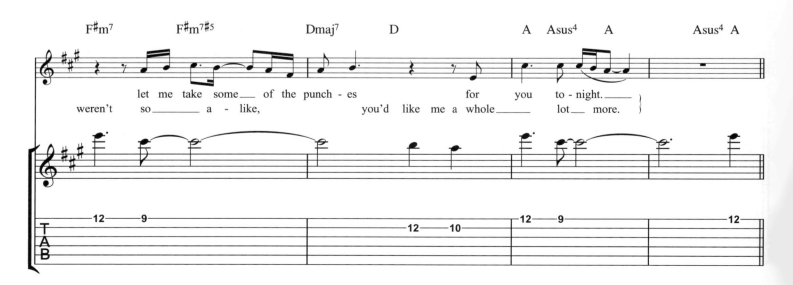

26

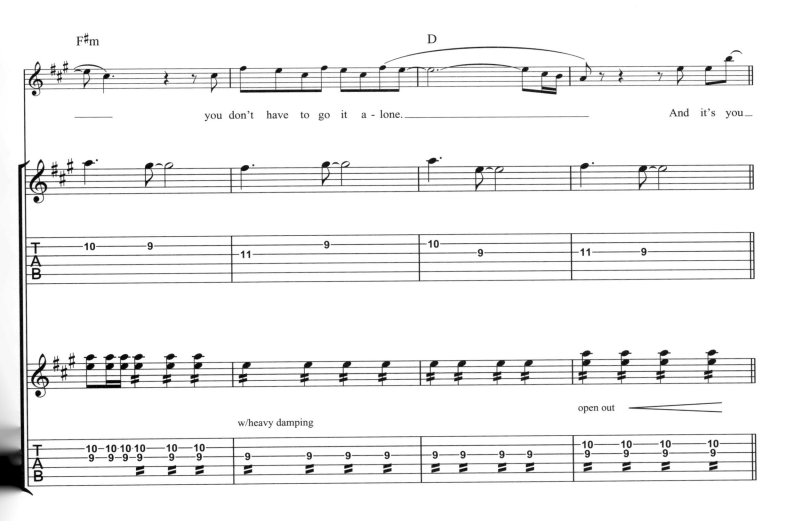

-times   you can't   make____ it   on_____

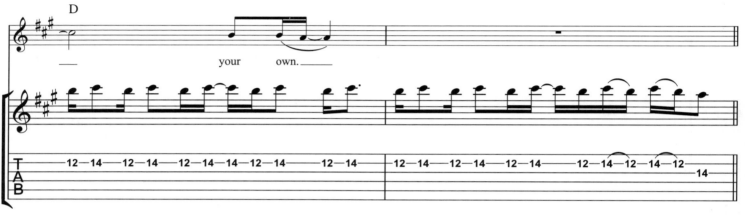

your own.____

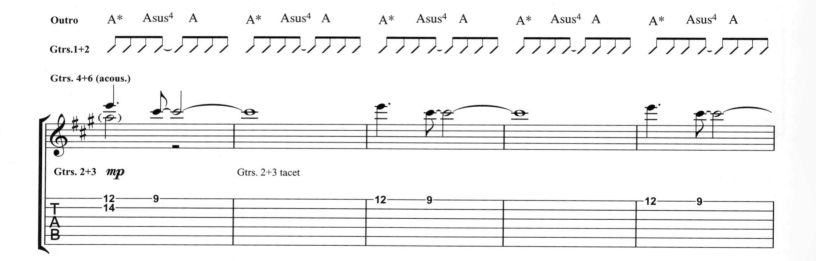

Outro

Gtrs.1+2

Gtrs. 4+6 (acous.)

Gtrs. 2+3 *mp*   Gtrs. 2+3 tacet

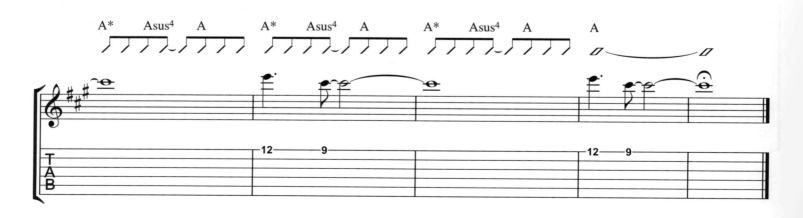

City Of Blinding Lights

Words by Bono
Music by U2

All gtrs. tuned down a semitone

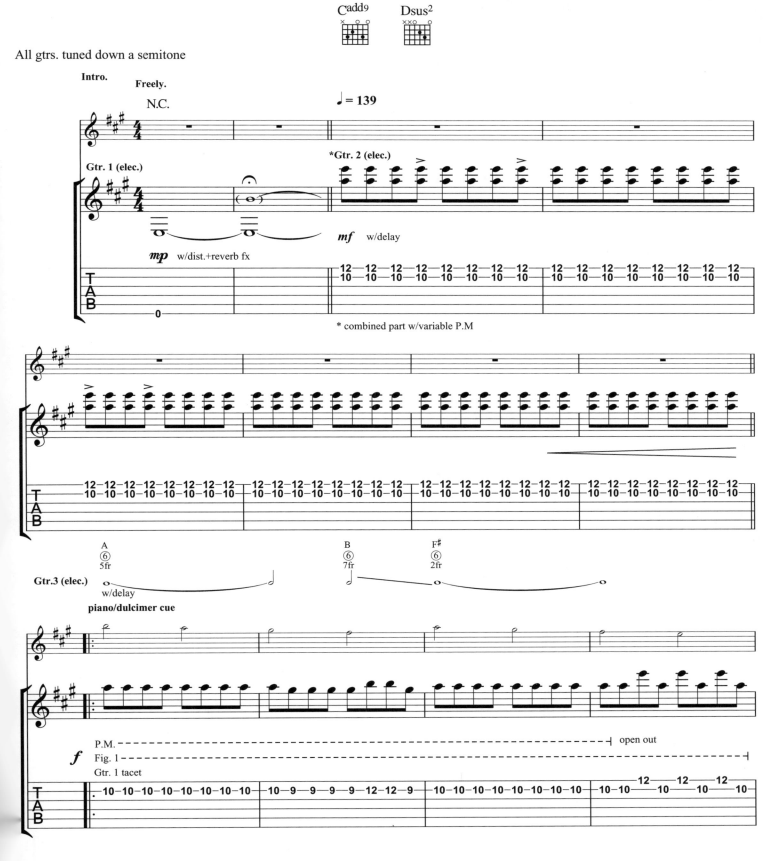

* combined part w/variable P.M

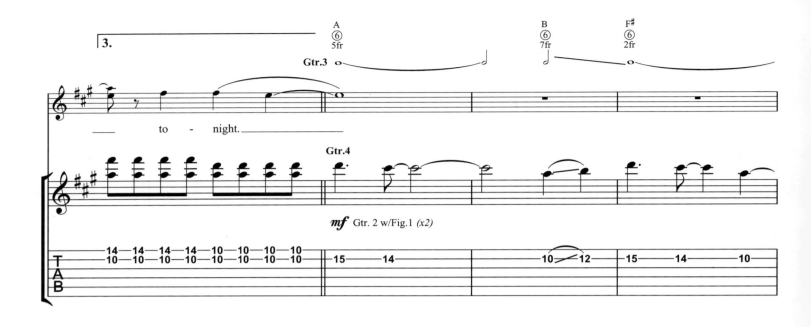

to - night.

In ___ the ci - ty _____ of blind - ing lights. _____

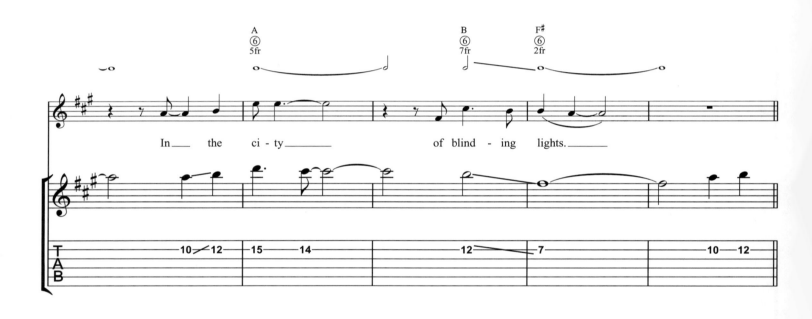

The more you know the less you feel, some pray _ for, oth - ers steal, _

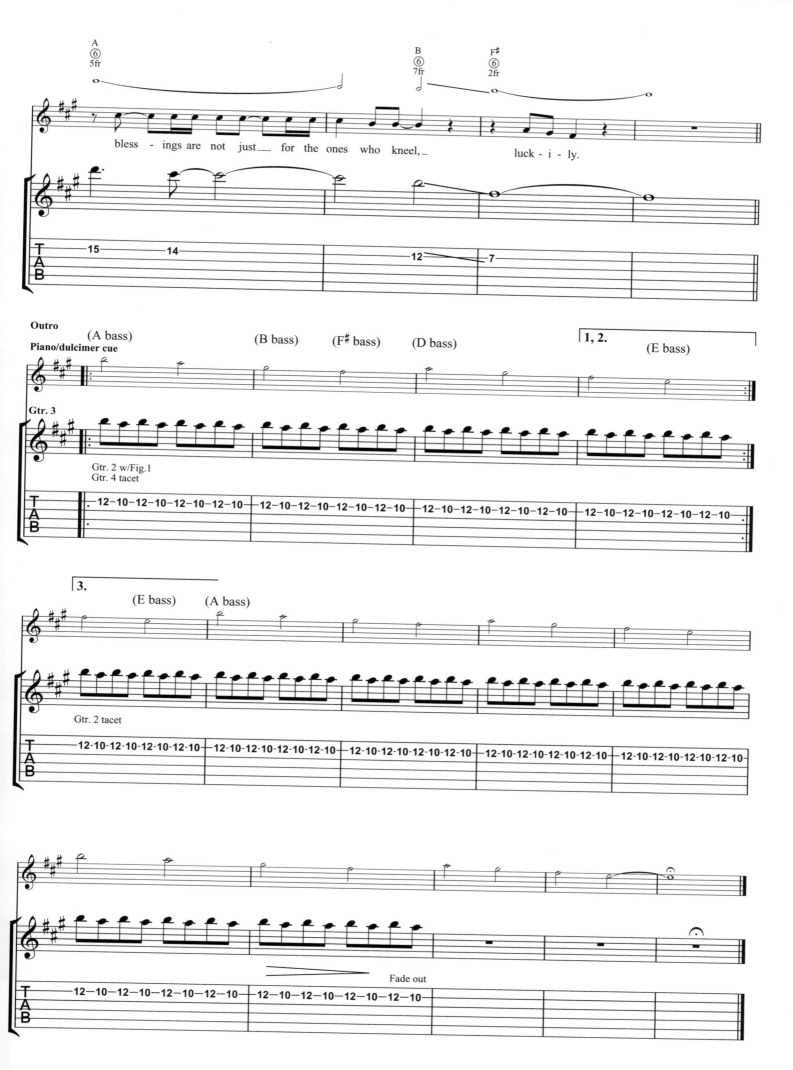

Love And Peace Or Else

Words by Bono & The Edge
Music by U2

Tune 6th string to D

All Because Of You

Words by Bono
Music by U2

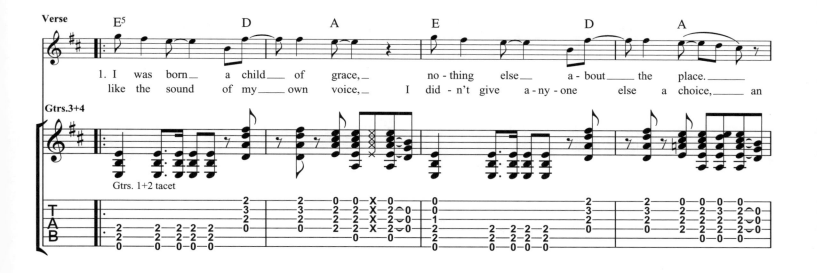

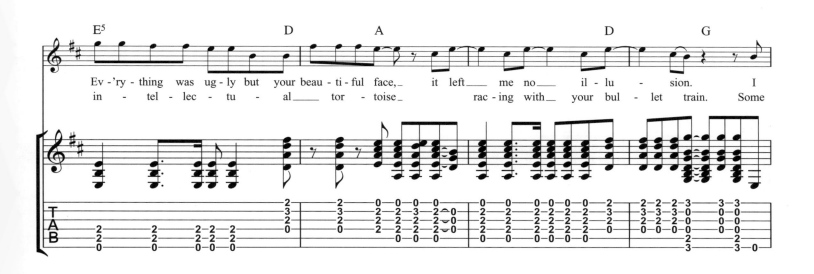

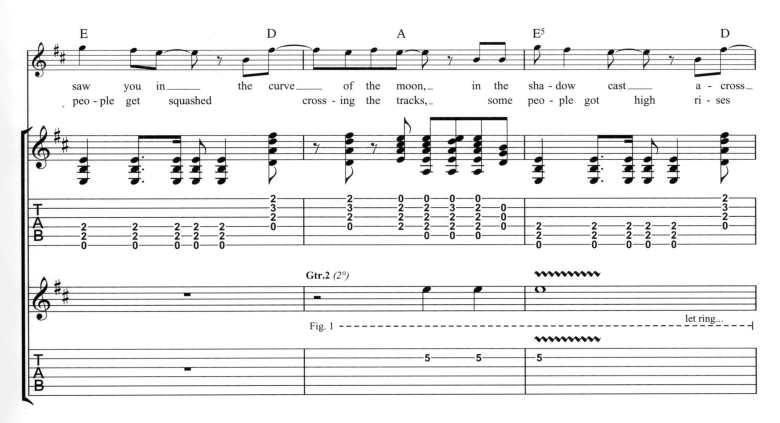

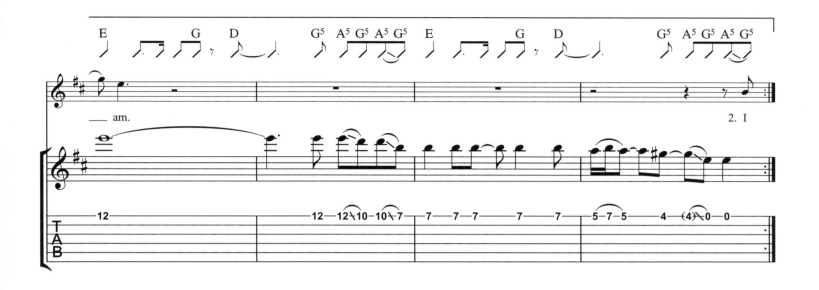

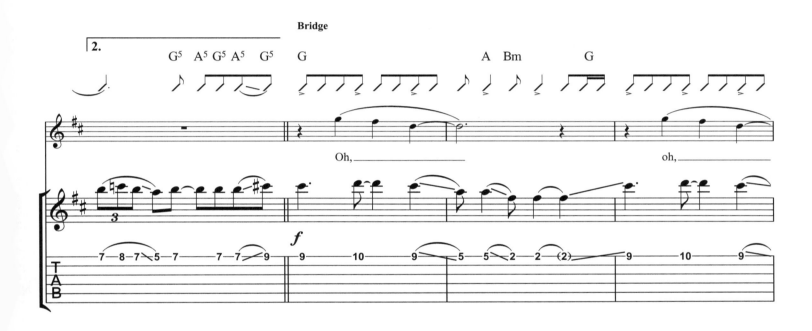

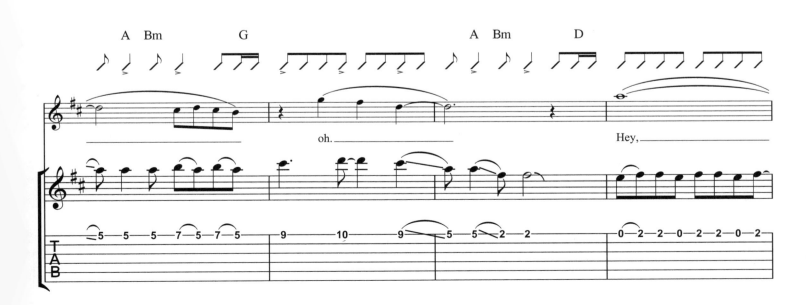

Crumbs From Your Table

Words by Bono
Music by U2

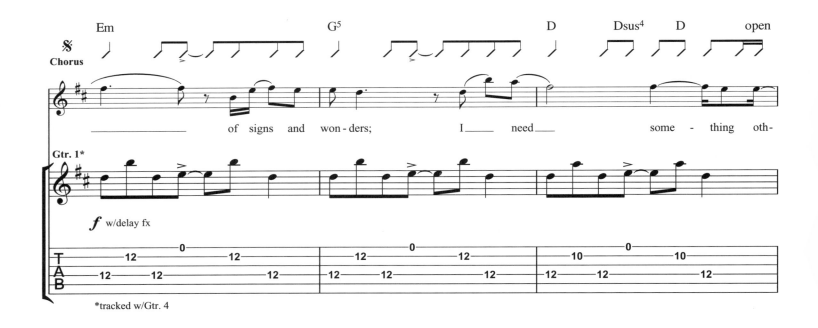

of signs and won-ders; I need some-thing oth-

*tracked w/Gtr. 4

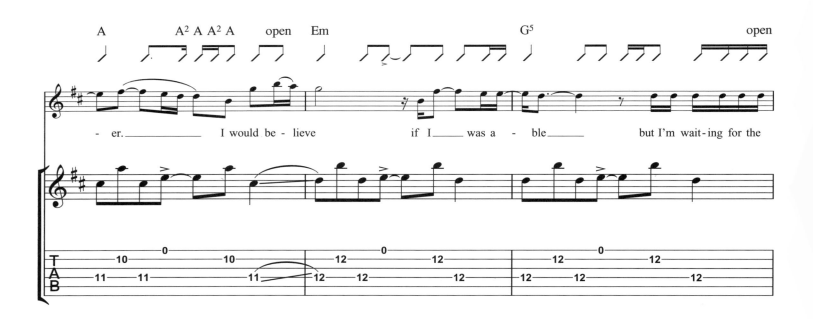

-er. I would be-lieve if I was a-ble but I'm wait-ing for the

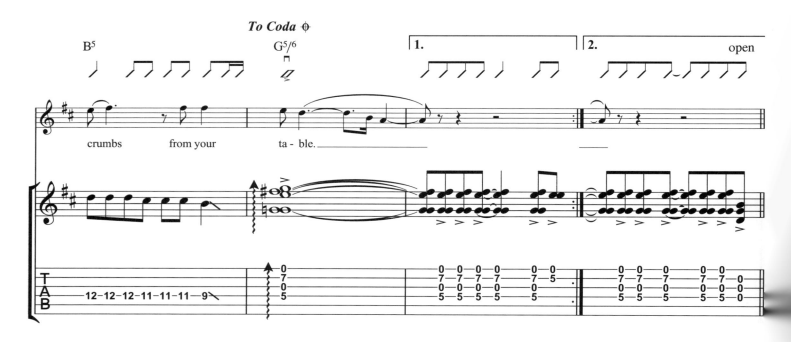

crumbs from your ta-ble.

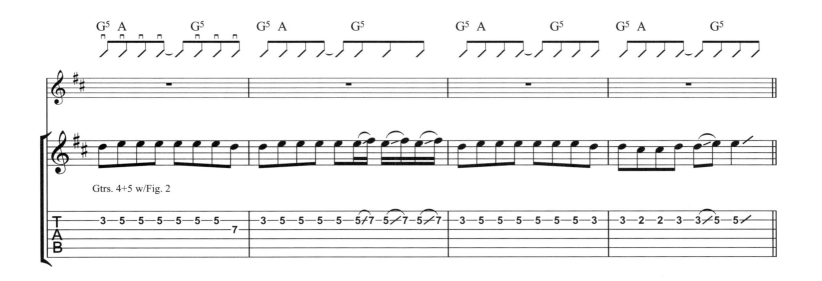

Bridge

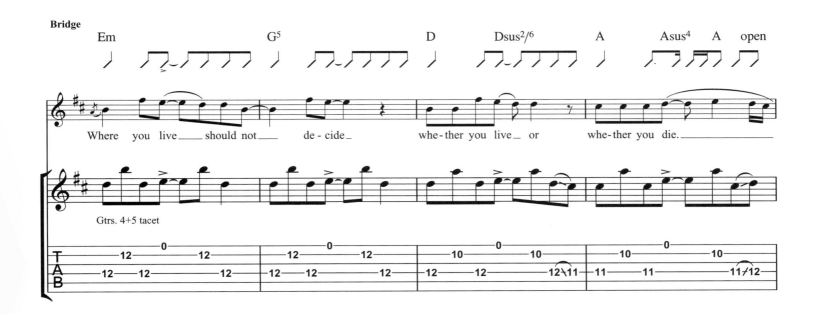

Where you live____ should not____ de-cide____ whe-ther you live__ or whe-ther you die.____

Gtrs. 4+5 tacet

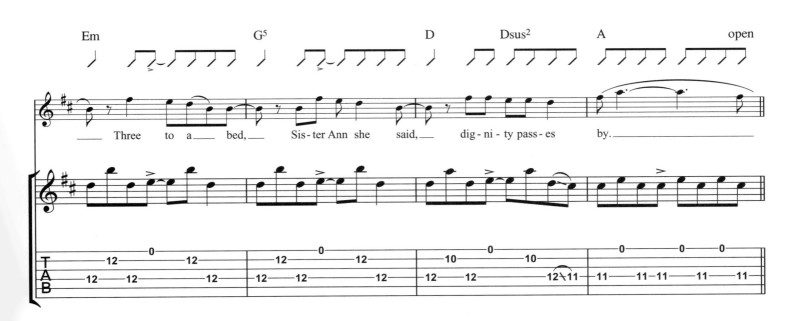

____ Three to a__ bed,____ Sis-ter Ann she said,____ dig-ni-ty pass-es by.____

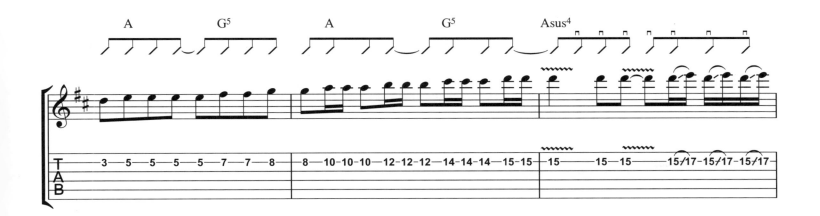

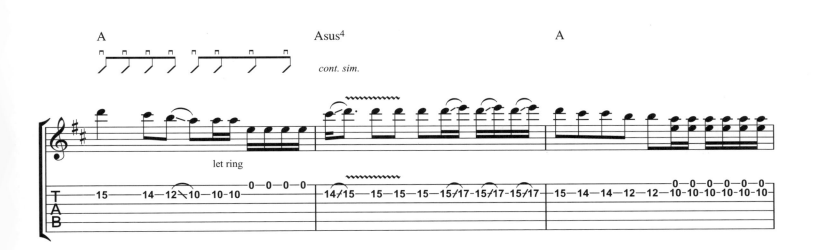

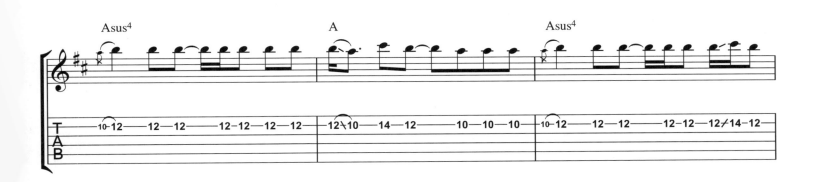

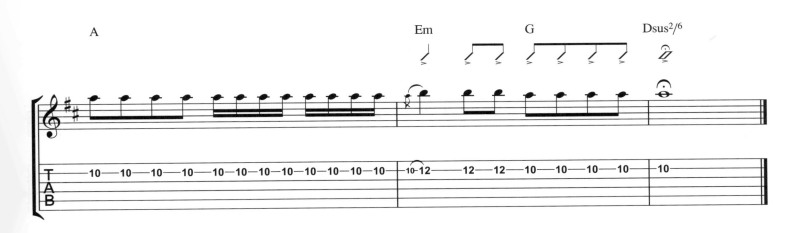

A Man And A Woman

Words by Bono
Music by U2

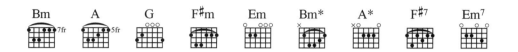

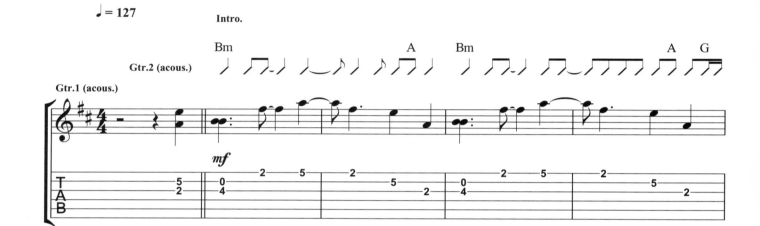

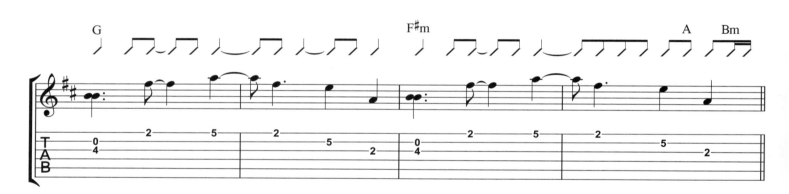

to - day, take the heat from_ the sun._
find you, catch you by_ the heel._
a - gain like a_ stray_ dog.

And lit - tle_ sis - ter,_ I know that ev -'ry - thing_ is not_
But you can't be numb for love, _ the on - ly pain is to feel
Lit - tle_ sis - ter,_ I've been try'n' to feel com-

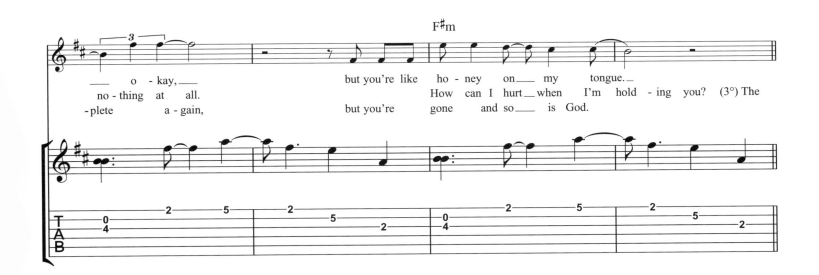

o - kay, but you're like ho - ney on_ my tongue._
no - thing at all. How can I hurt_ when I'm hold - ing you? (3°) The
-plete a - gain, but you're gone and so_ is God.

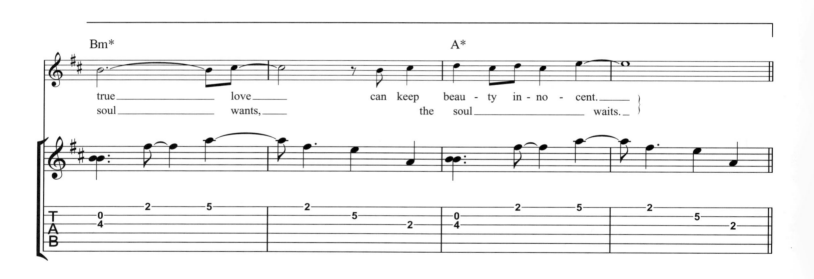

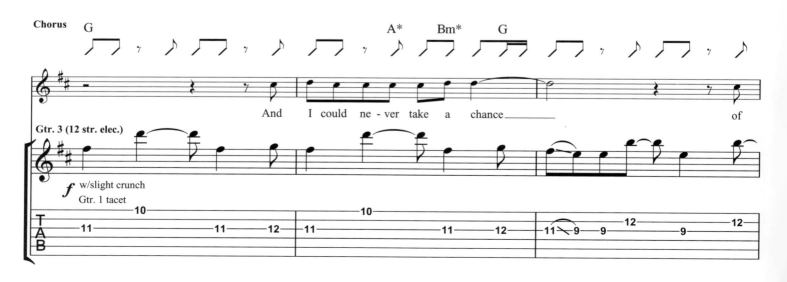

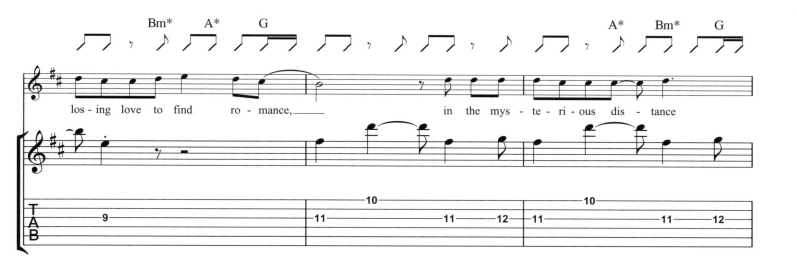

los - ing love to find ro - mance,_____ in the mys - te - ri - ous dis - tance

be - tween a man and__ a wo - man.

No   I   could ne - ver take a chance,__
And you're the one, there's no one else,____
For love and sex and faith and fear_____

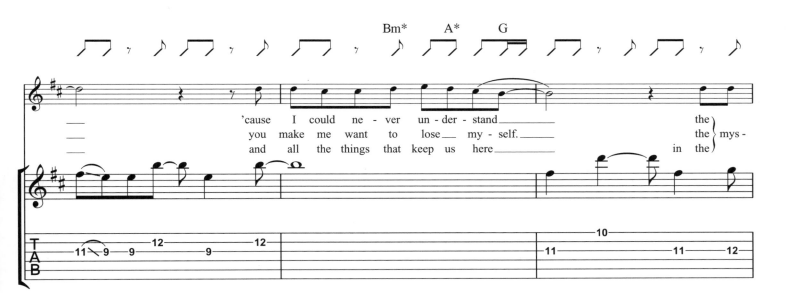

___ 'cause I could ne - ver un - der - stand_____ the mys -
___ you make me want to lose__ my - self._____
___ and all the things that keep us here_____ in the

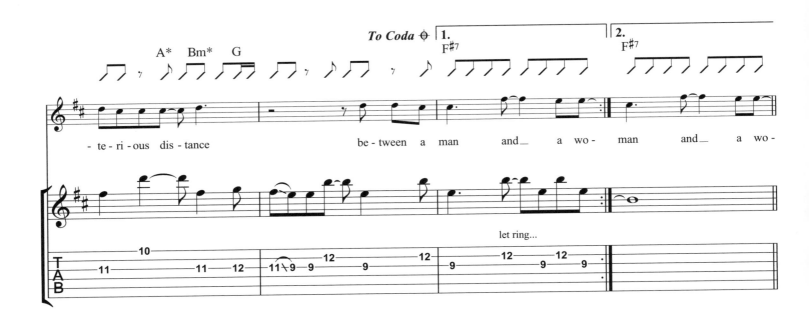

-te - ri -ous dis - tance   be - tween a man   and__ a wo - man   and__ a wo-

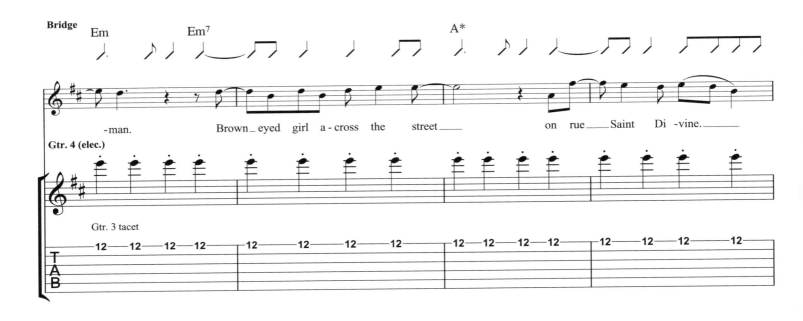

-man.   Brown__eyed girl a - cross the   street____   on rue____Saint   Di -vine.____

I   thought this   is   the   one   for   me,____   but she was al -

One Step Closer

Words by Bono
Music by U2

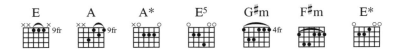

*combined part w/pedal steel gtr.

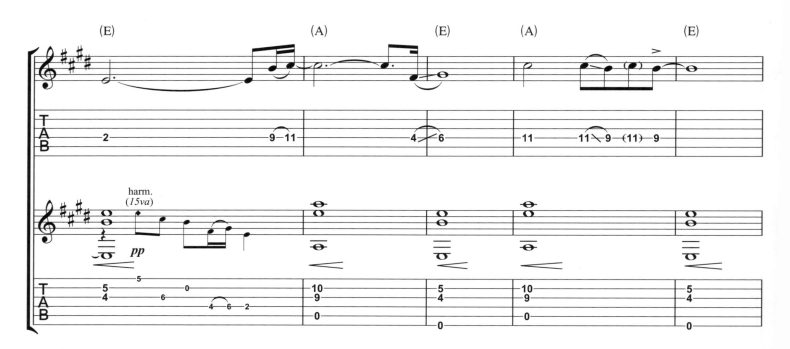

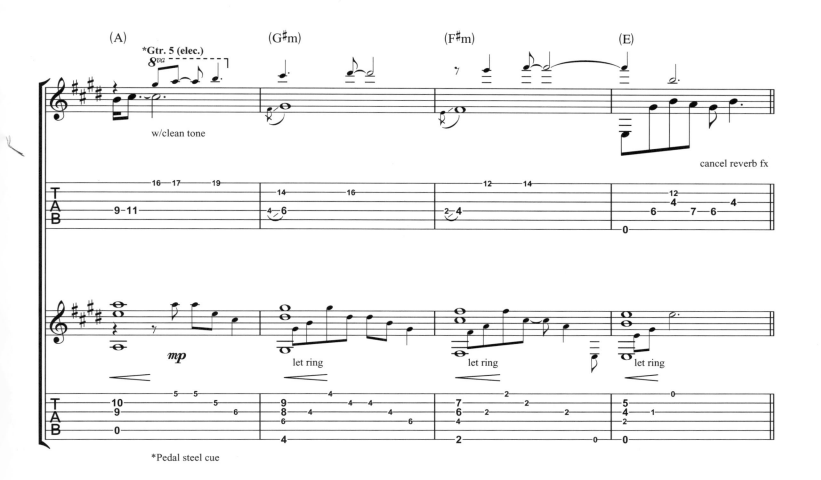

*Pedal steel cue

Verse

1. I'm 'round the cor - ner from a - ny - thing____ that's

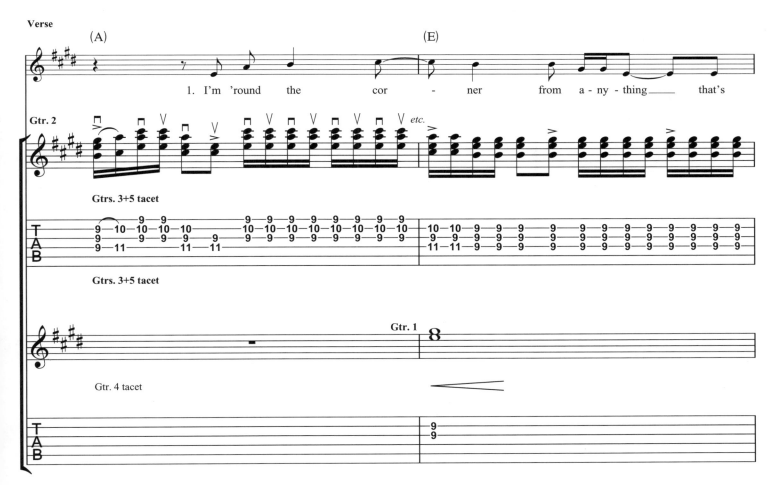

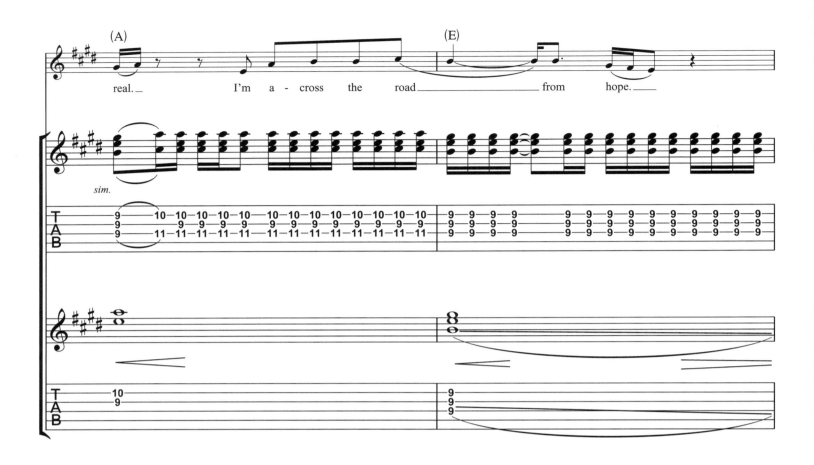

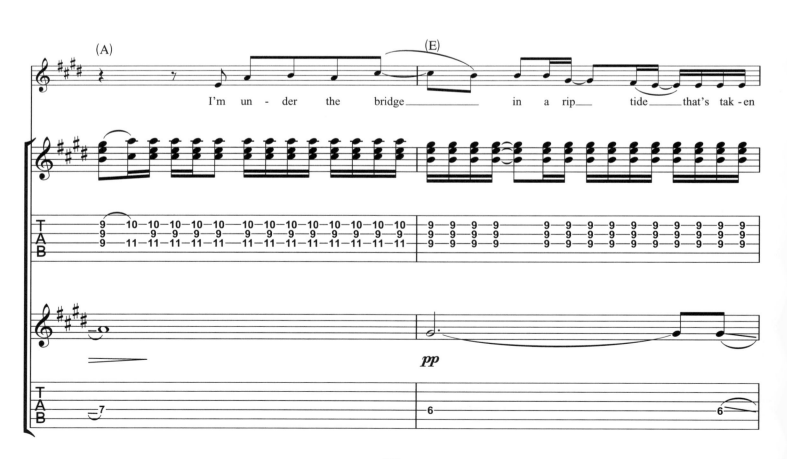

72

Original Of The Species

Words by Bono
Music by U2

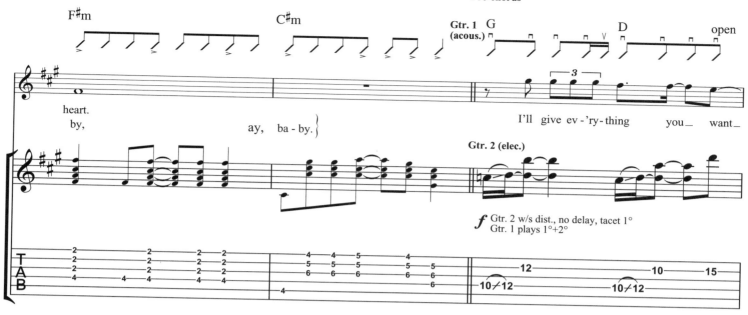

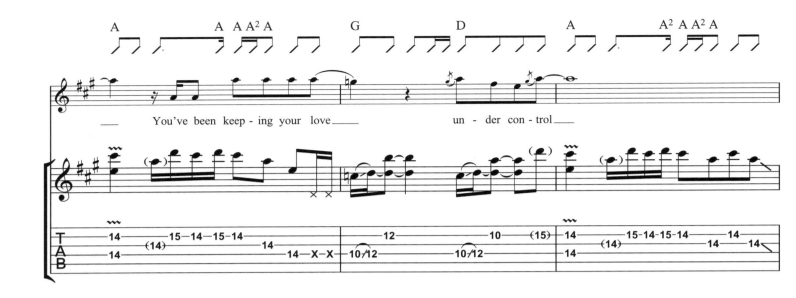

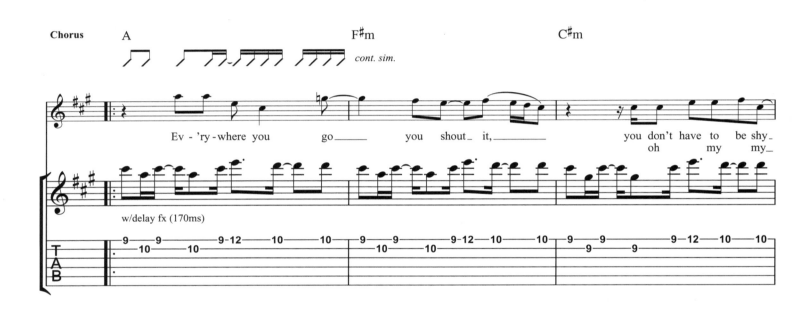

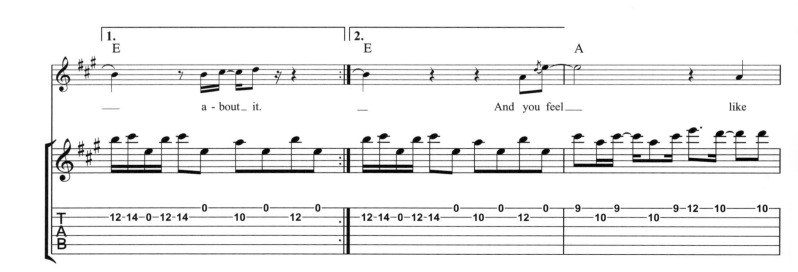

Yahweh

Words by Bono & The Edge
Music by U2

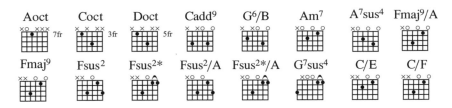

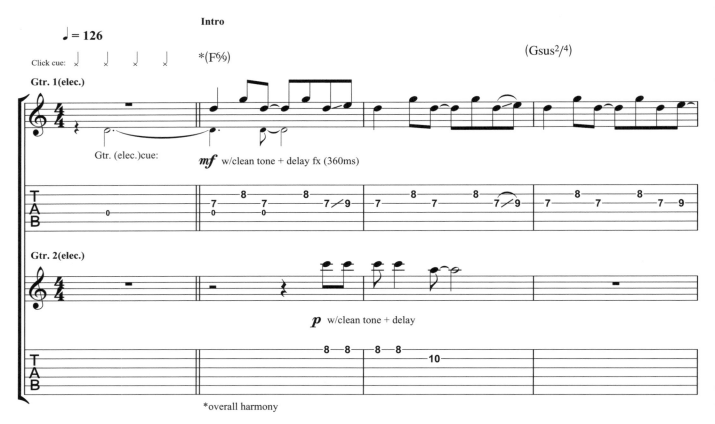

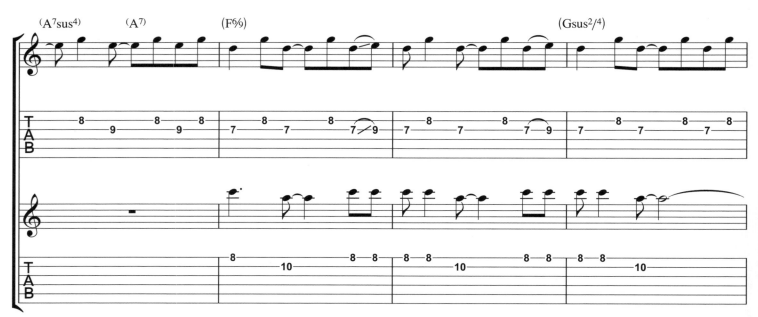

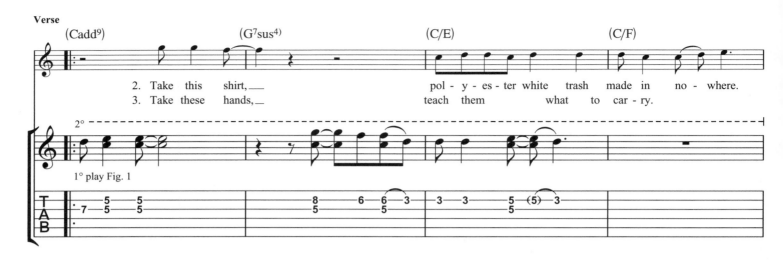

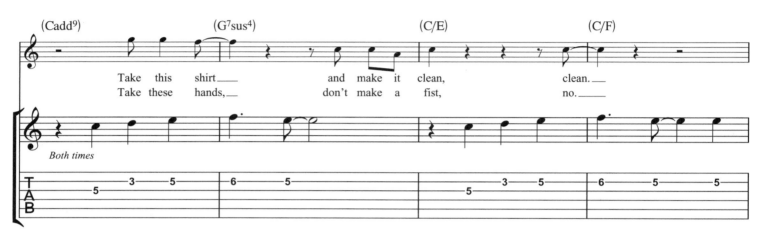

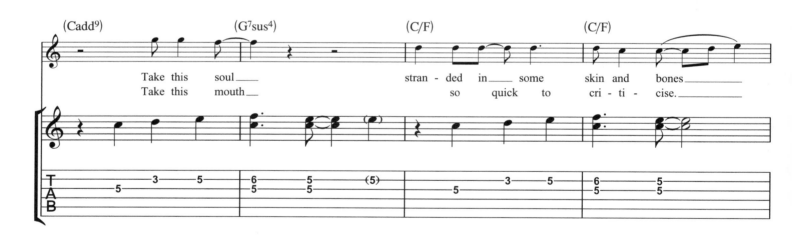

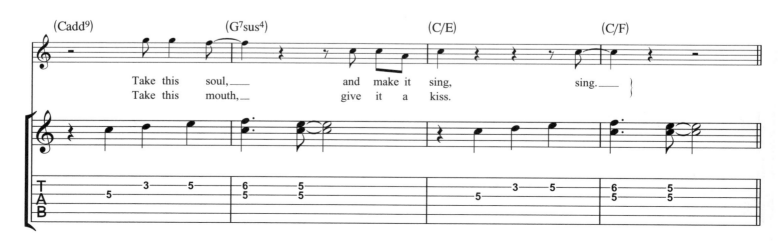

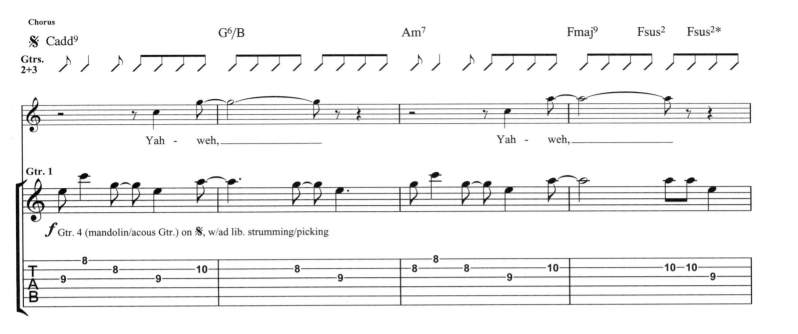

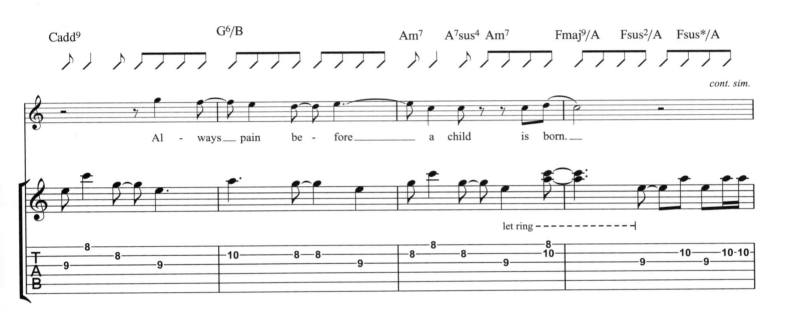

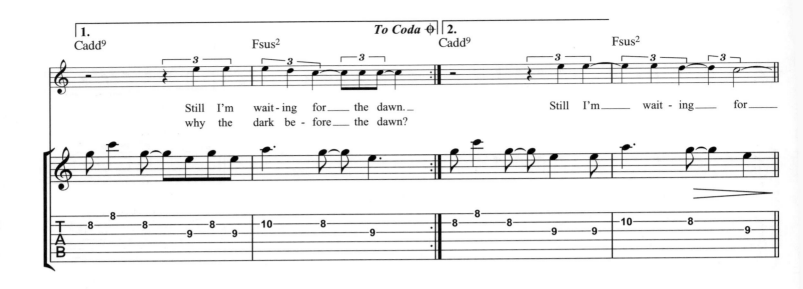

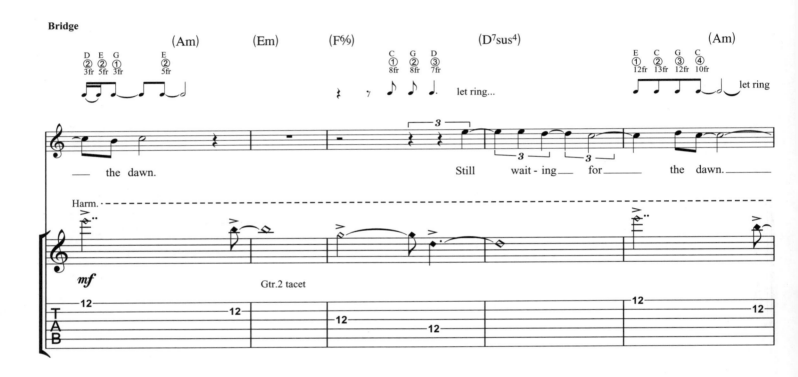

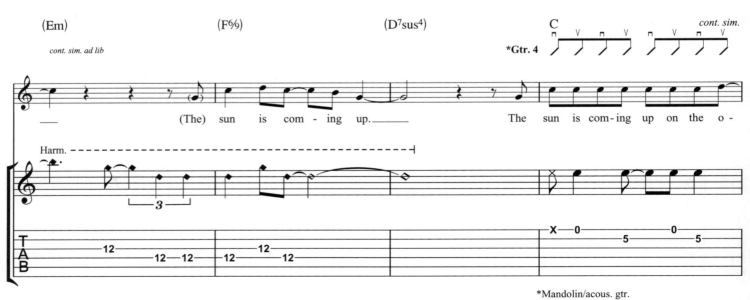

*Mandolin/acous. gtr.

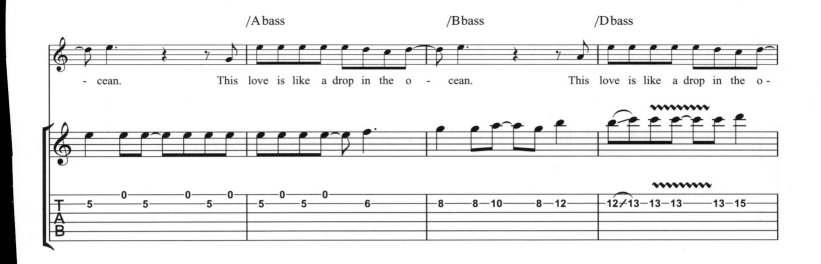

/A bass   /B bass   /D bass

- cean.   This love is like a drop in the o - cean.   This love is like a drop in the o -

D.S. al Coda

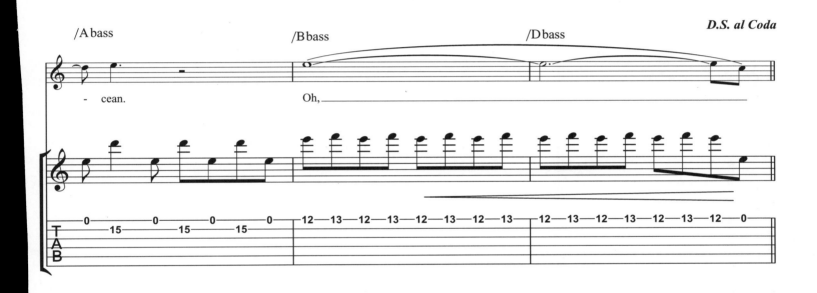

/A bass   /B bass   /D bass

- cean.   Oh,_____

Coda

Cadd⁹   G⁷sus⁴   C/E

cont. *sim.*

Oh   ooh oh   ooh   oh   ooh oh   ooh   oh._____

oh   ooh oh   ooh oh   ooh oh   ooh

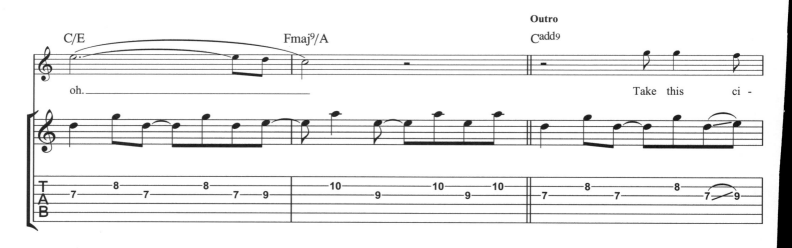

oh._____   Take this   ci -

Outro

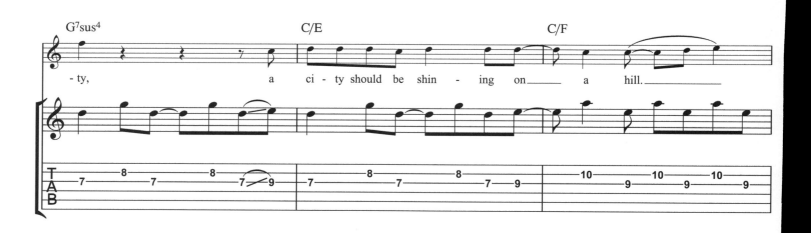

- ty,   a   ci - ty should be shin - ing on___ a   hill._____

Take this   ci - ty,   if   it   be   your___ will.

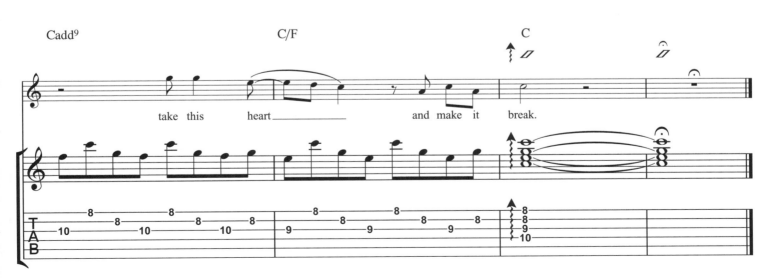

Fast Cars

Words by Bono & The Edge
Music by U2

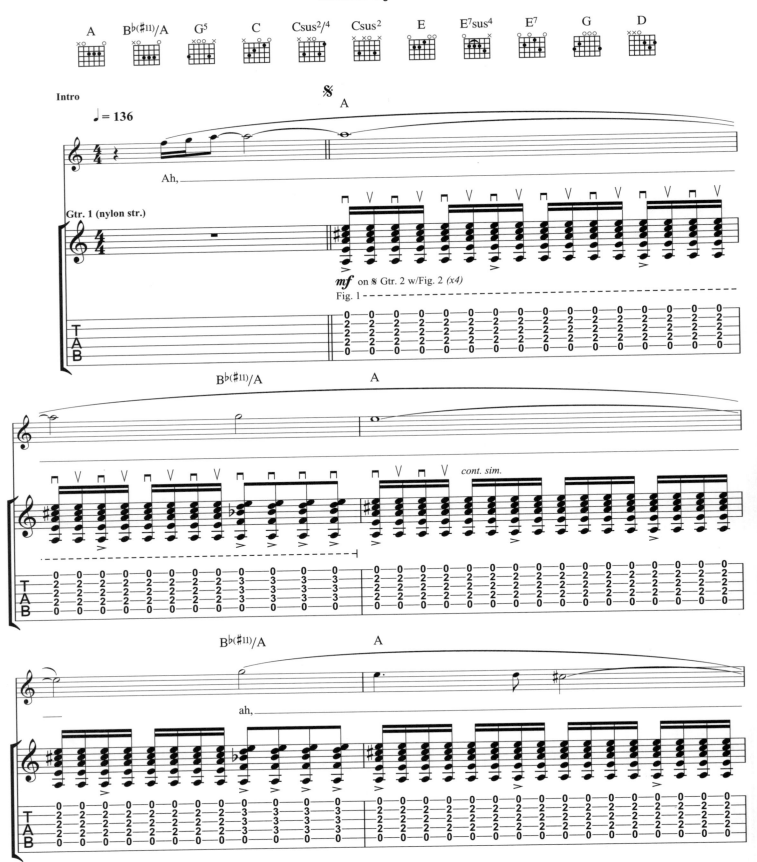

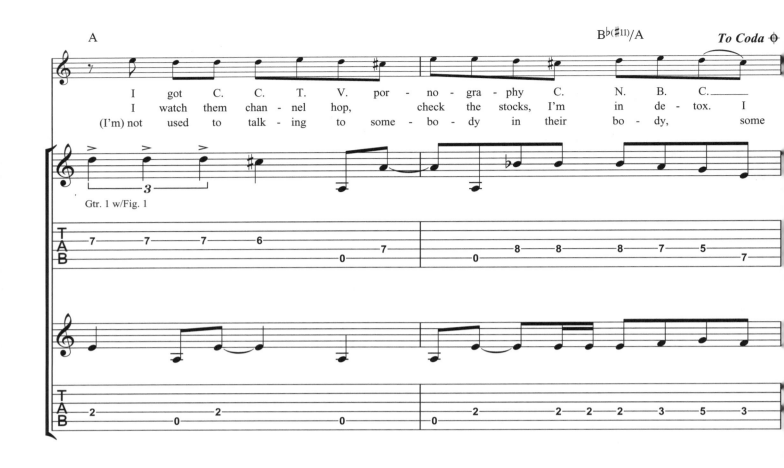

I   got   C.   C.   T.   V.   por - no - gra - phy   C.   N.   B.   C._____
I   watch   them   chan - nel   hop,   check   the   stocks,   I'm   in   de - tox.   I
(I'm) not   used   to   talk - ing   to   some - bo - dy   in   their   bo - dy,   some

Gtr. 1 w/Fig. 1

I   got   the   night - ly   news   to   get   to   know   the   en - e - my.   }
want   the   lot   of   what   you've   got,   what   you've   got   can   make   this   stop.   }

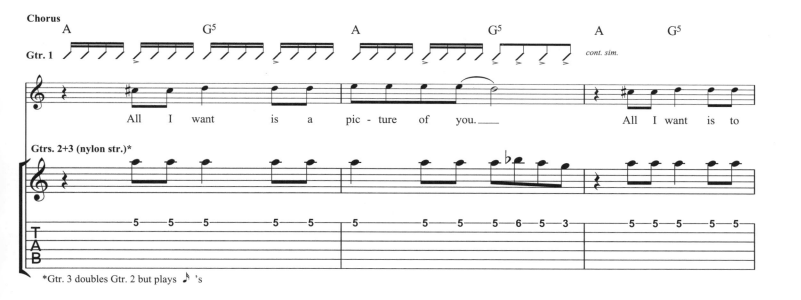

*Gtr. 3 doubles Gtr. 2 but plays ♪ 's

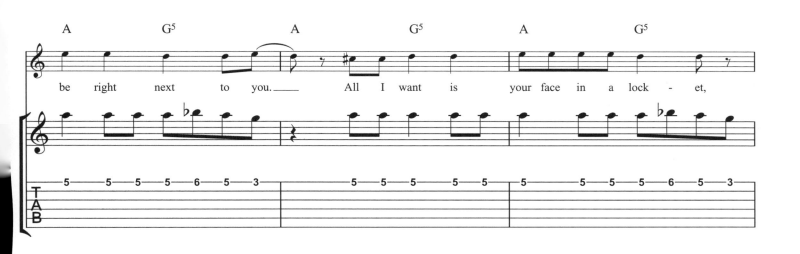

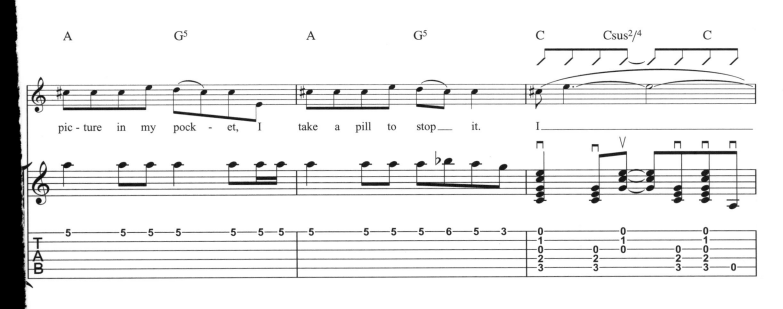